Story

I can read the Speed sounds.

I can read the Green words.

I can read the Red words.

I can read the story.

I can answer the questions about the story.

I can read the Speed words.

Say the Speed sounds

Consonants

Ask your child to say the sounds (not the letter names) clearly and quickly, in and out of order. Make sure he or she does not add 'uh' to the end of the sounds, e.g. 'f' not 'fuh'.

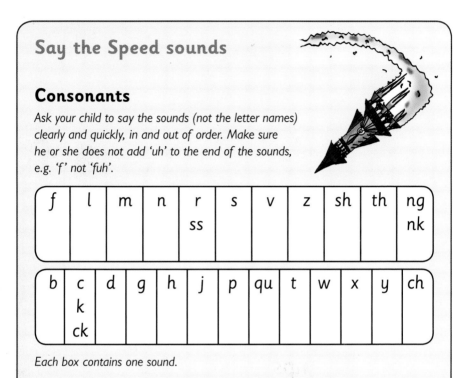

f	l	m	n	r ss	s	v	z	sh	th	ng nk

b	c k ck	d	g	h	j	p	qu	t	w	x	y	ch

Each box contains one sound.

Vowels

Ask your child to say each vowel sound and then the word, e.g. 'a', 'at'.

at	hen	in	on	up

Story 1 Fat frog

Read the Green words

For each word ask your child to read the separate sounds, e.g. 'f-r-o-g', 'b-a-nk' and then blend the sounds together to make the word, e.g. 'frog', 'bank'. Sometimes one sound is represented by more than one letter, e.g. 'th', 'ck', 'sh'. These are underlined.

fat   frog   in   from   pond

ba<u>n</u>k   spla<u>sh</u>

Ask you child to read the root word first and then the word with the ending.

ki<u>ck</u> → ki<u>ck</u>s   leg → legs

jump → jumps   land → lands

Read the Red words

Red words don't sound like they look. Read the word out to your child. Explain that he or she will have to stop and think about how to say the red word in the story.

<u>th</u>e

Story 1
Fat frog

Introduction
This is a story about a frog making a splash.

A fat frog kicks
its legs . . .

and jumps from the bank.

It lands in the pond.

Splash!

Ask your child:
What happens to the duck?

Story ② I have lost . . .

Read the Green words

*For each word ask your child to read the separate sounds, e.g. 'l-o-s-t',
'd-o-ll' and then blend the sounds together to make the word, e.g. 'lost', 'doll'.
Sometimes one sound is represented by more than one letter, e.g. 've', 'll', 'ck'.
These are underlined.*

lost   ha<u>ve</u>   do<u>ll</u>   not   tru<u>ck</u>

pen   ted   and

Read the Red words

*Red words don't sound like they look. Read the words out to your child.
Explain that he or she will have to stop and think about how to say the
red words in the story.*

I   my

Story ⭐2
I have lost ...

Introduction

Have you ever lost a toy? This is a story about a girl who loses her toys ...

I have lost a truck.

I have lost a doll and
a pen.

I have not lost my ted.

Ask your child:
⭐ *What three things has the girl lost?*

Story ⟨3⟩ Chips

Read the Green words

*For each word ask your child to read the separate sounds, e.g. 'c-a-n',
'ch-i-p-s' and then blend the sounds together to make the word, e.g. 'can',
'chips'. Sometimes one sound is represented by more than one letter, e.g. 'ch',
've'. These are underlined.*

crisps   can   pop   ha<u>ve</u>   <u>ch</u>ips

Mum

Read the Red words

*Red words don't sound like they look. Read the words out to your child.
Explain that he or she will have to stop and think about how to say the
red words in the story.*

no   I

Story ③
Chips

Introduction
This is a story about a boy who wants to eat chips.

Can I have chips?
No.

Can I have pop?
No.

Can I have crisps?
No.
Oh, Mum.

Ask your child:
What three things does the boy
want to have?

Story ④ I am sick

Read the Green words

For each word ask your child to read the separate sounds, e.g. 't-u-m', 'ch-i-n' and then blend the sounds together to make the word, e.g. 'tum', 'chin'. Sometimes one sound is represented by more than one letter, e.g. 'ck', 've', 'ch'. These are underlined.

bed   si<u>ck</u>   am   ha<u>ve</u>   <u>ch</u>in   ne<u>ck</u>

tum   mum   get   spots

Read the Red words

Red words don't sound like they look. Read the words out to your child. Explain that he or she will have to stop and think about how to say the red words in the story.

I   my

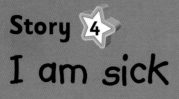
I am sick

Introduction

Have you ever felt poorly? This is a story about a little girl who is covered in spots.

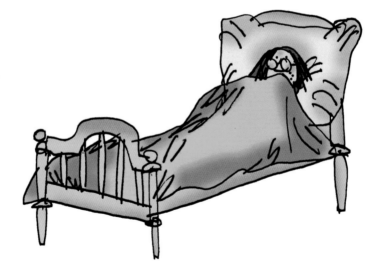

I am in bed.

I have got spots on my chin, on my neck and on my tum.

I am sick.
Get my mum.

Ask your child:
⭐ *What does the little girl want?*

Speed words for Story ⭐1

Ask your child to read the words across the rows, down the columns and in and out of order, clearly and quickly.

fat	frog	in	pond	lands
bank	the	kicks	jumps	legs

Speed words for Story ⭐2

I	have	doll	my	truck
pen	lost	ted	and	not

Speed words for Story ⟨3⟩

Ask your child to read the words across the rows, down the columns and in and out of order, clearly and quickly.

no	crisps	can	have
pop	I	chips	Mum

Speed words for Story ⟨4⟩

am	have	chin	I	bed
sick	neck	tum	get	my